What's in a Name?
A Tale of Discovery

Keishia Lee Louis

Publisher: Precocious Pupil Press, an imprint of RelaSonship, LLC
Dacula, GA 30019

ISBN: 978-1-7334966-7-4

Library of Congress Control Number: 2021925255

Written and Illustrated by Keishia Lee Louis
Character Design: Graphic Mama, Inc.

To Mannayah, Eleazar, and Maranatha.
Mom loves you lots!

There were three things in this world that
Makeda could not stand: Brussels sprouts, math
and her name.

Brussels, Belgium

Brussels sprouts. Sure they were named for a famous city, in a famous country, known for the best chocolate in the world.

And sure, they look cute, like little cabbages, which taste okay.

But they certainly did not taste like chocolate (or even cabbage). How did so many people in Brussels like them? Yuck!

Daddy always said, "God created them, Mama prepared them, and you're going to eat them."

"Why would God create such a sneaky little vegetable?" she thought.

Math. It wasn't that she did not understand it. She was actually great at it. Many times she could come up with the answers faster than the other students in the class. The reason she did not like math was that being great did not come easy like her other subjects. It was too much work and boring, besides.

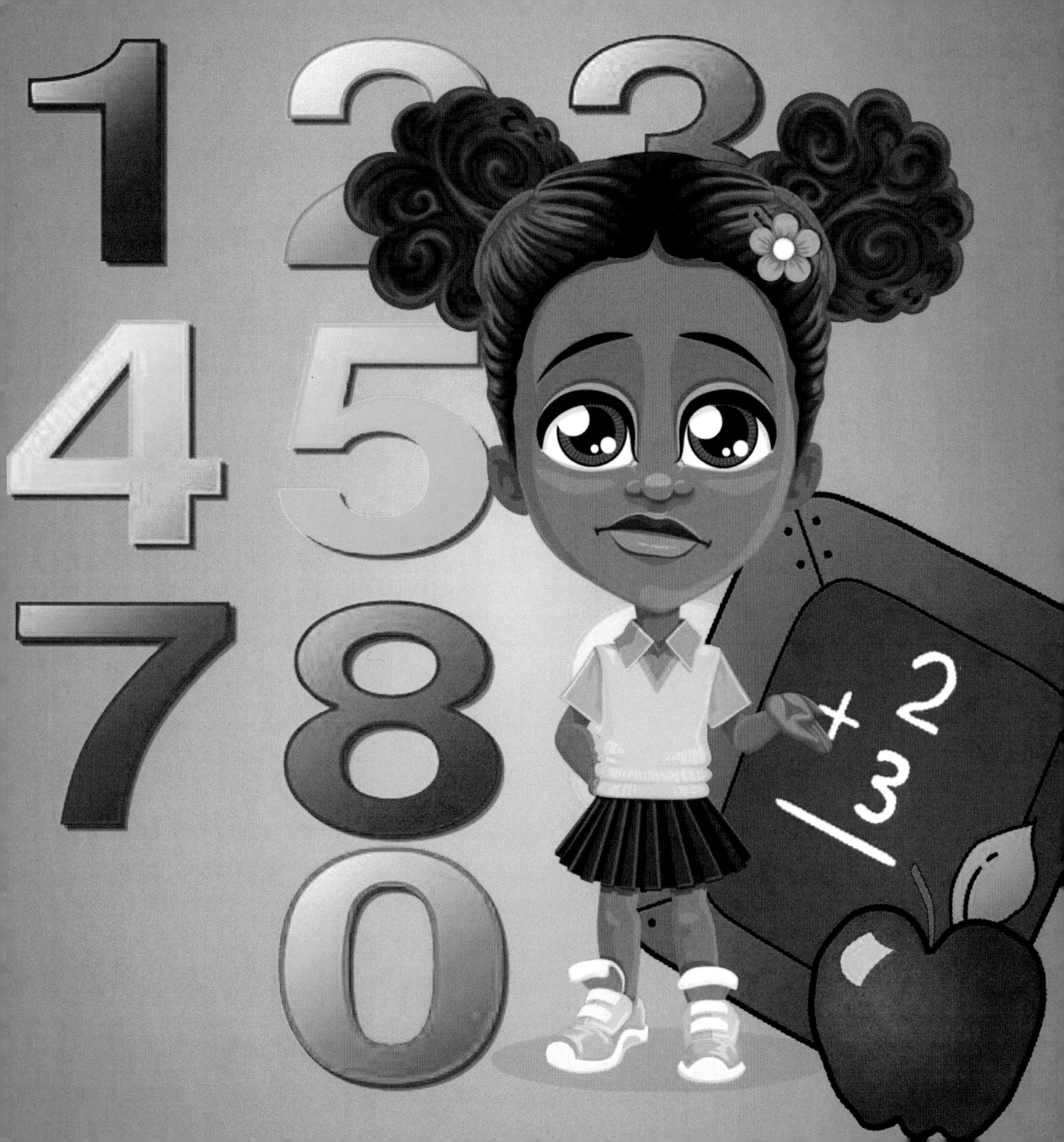
1 2 3
4 5
7 8
0
+ 2
3

And then there was her name: Makeda. She felt as though her parents threw some words into a letter scrambling machine, pushed some buttons to form a secret code and voilá: Makeda. The problem was that she did not know how to solve the code.

"Mama, why am I named Makeda?"

"It was my grandmother's name, and we named you after her because we loved her very much."

Although Makeda loved Mama and Daddy, she did not know her mother's father's mother. It was too much. She did not think the name fit her very well.

"Maybe I can try a new name," she thought.

Why can't people name themselves?" she asked one night at dinner.

"Some people do, when they are old enough," said Daddy.

"Am I old enough?"

"You want to change your name?" Mama was a little shocked.

"I don't think it fits me."

"Hmm… Well if someone is old enough to eat Brussels sprouts without complaining, I guess she could be old enough to try out a new name."

Makeda cleaned her plate without saying one word about the sneaky vegetables that had made their way onto her plate. Mama smiled and Daddy laughed.

"So what name are you going to choose?"

"I think Sophia is nice. It sounds like a princess' name."

The next day at school Makeda boldly proclaimed, "You can now call me Sophia, Mrs. Gauss."

"Sophia?" Mrs. Gauss looked surprised.

"Makeda, I mean Sophia is trying out a new name," explained Daddy.

"Well Sophia is a great name: full of wisdom," said Mrs. Gauss. "It's funny that you--one of my best math students--would choose that name," she exclaimed.

"I just read about a Russian woman named Sophia Kovalevskaya, who lived during a time when many people thought that women could not be good at math. Yet, despite it all, she became a famous mathematician and professor."

Daddy smiled. Makeda shuddered. How could Mrs. Gauss ruin such a good name?

"Okay, Sophia's out," she thought to herself.

"Thank you for letting me know, Mrs. Gauss." Makeda slumped to her desk.

The next day, Makeda was determined to try a new name. She rushed down the stairs and was surprised to see her brother Mekhai in the kitchen. He was home from college.

"Glad you're finally up, Makeda. I wanted to play another round of checkers to get my champion title back," he smiled.

"I'm not Makeda. I'm Kate," she said as a matter of fact. "And checkers sounds great, but you know I'm going to beat you." She laughed.

"A lot has changed since I left. How long have you been Kate?" He asked.

"A little while..." She answered sheepishly.

"Kate is a nice name. One of my mentors at Johns Hopkins is named Kate Okikiolu. She has won many prizes for her work in the field of math." Mekhai said.

"Oh no! Not that again." Makeda rolled her eyes.

"She even won $500,000. It was an award from the president for math and science research. She also helped kids get better in math while she was at the University of California in San Diego. I'm going to try to win it one day, too." He said it proudly.

"Hmm... Meeting the president? $500,000? Wait that's half a million dollars! That's a lot of money for being good at math and helping kids. That didn't sound too bad, but teaching and learning math for the rest of her life? Not very exciting," she thought.

The next day, Āyati (granddad) came to visit. Makeda loved being with Āyati because he would always teach her how to bake a new delicious treat. This time it was his famous double decker chocolate fudge cake.

"Makeda, how much butter do we need?"

"It says eight ounces." Makeda replied.

"How many sticks is that?"

"Let me see... Eight ounces equals one cup and the marks on the side of the butter say each stick equals half a cup. So we'll need two sticks." Makada said.

After they finished mixing and putting the batter into the pan, they put the cake in the oven.

"Āyati, why do you call me Makeda?"

"Your mama told me you don't think your name fits you anymore. Let me tell you a story. My mama and daddy were from Ethiopia. In Ethiopia, many people love the name Makeda. Now, I'm not saying you should love it because other people do, but let me tell you why they do."

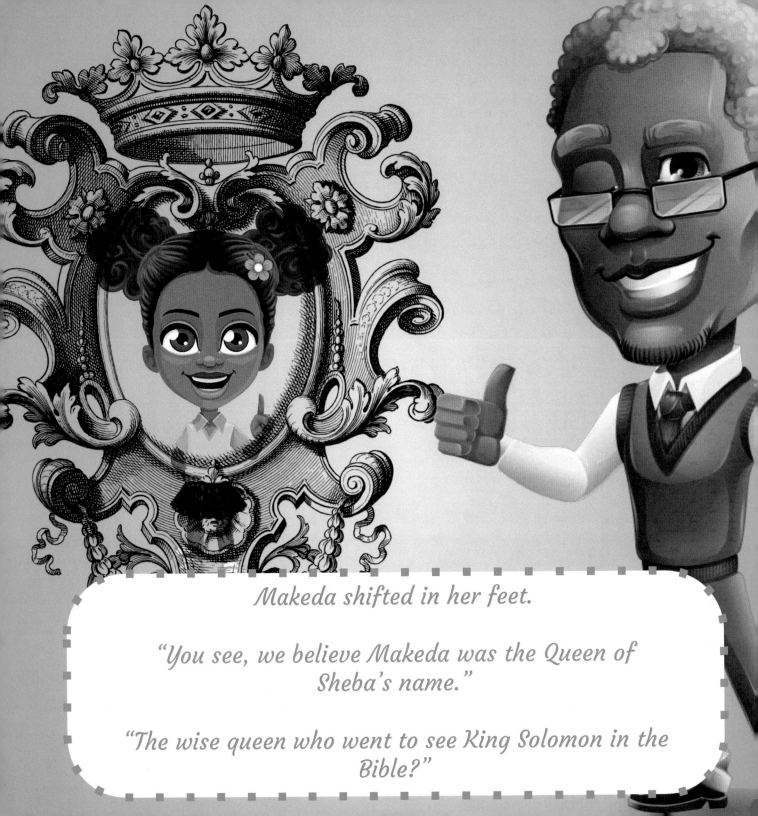

Makeda shifted in her feet.

"You see, we believe Makeda was the Queen of Sheba's name."

"The wise queen who went to see King Solomon in the Bible?"

"That's the one. She was determined to test his wisdom. When she saw that he was truly a wise man, she fell in love with him. Next thing you know, she starts believing in Solomon's God, the God of the Bible. They got married and had a son, Menelik the First. He was the leader of the first royal dynasty in Ethiopia."

"Really?"

"That's what we believe. Before Menelik the First ruled Ethiopia, many people worshipped the sun among other gods."

"Like the Egyptians?"

"Yes, but the new king worshipped only one God like his father, King Solomon. This is where the roots of our faith begin."

"Oh, I see," Makeda sat up a little straighter.

"You didn't know so much could be packed into one name."

She shook her head.

"I think you are a lot like that first Queen Makeda."

"Really?"

"Yes. My mother was a strong woman and her parents knew that she would need a strong name.

"Was she strong like Queen Makeda, the Queen of Sheba?"

"Yes, in her own way. Your parents saw the same strength in you and knew that you would need a strong name."

"You think I'm strong?"

"I certainly do. Ready for some of that cake, Makeda? You don't mind if I call you that, do you?"

Makeda smiled. "I guess being Makeda is a pretty good thing."

Made in the USA
Columbia, SC
27 September 2022